HOME LEARNING

HODDER

Men Arithmetic

C000132534

AGE 9-11

Dr Bill Gillham

As a parent, you can play an important part in your child's education by your interest and encouragement. This book is designed to help you develop your child's ability in mental arithmetic. It will:

- help them to *understand* what goes on in arithmetic.
- help them to see that calculators can't do your thinking for you.
- make them more mentally agile. (You become intelligent by *using* your brain.)
- help them to avoid calculator mistakes because they will know roughly what the answer to a calculation should be. *Guess-estimating is as important as being exactly right.*
- help them to use arithmetic in practical, real-life situations.
- help them to become fluent in the four rules of arithmetic: addition, subtraction, multiplication and division.

The book is divided into seven sections, each containing four tests, the fourth of which is a check test. Finally there is an end-of-book test and a rating chart to show how well your child has done.

Hodder
Children's
Books

NCPTA

The only home learning programme supported by the NCPTA

How to help your child

- Don't expect them to do more than one test a day.

- Make sure they can read the words in the questions before they try to answer them.

- Explain that they must not work things out on paper – it has to be done in their heads!

- If they can't do a question after they've thought about it tell them to put a ? against it and to go on to the next one.

- The check test should be an oral test. Read the questions out loud for your child to answer without looking at the book.

- Mark the tests, being careful to use the 'nearly right' category.

- Go over mistakes by talking them through, not working them out on paper.

- Give plenty of praise. Children thrive on success!

> 1 kilogramme (kg) = 1000 grammes (g)
> 1 kilometre (km) = 1000 metres (m)
> 1 metre (m) = 100 centimetres (cm)
> 1 centimetre (cm) = 10 millimetres (mm)

The right of Dr Bill Gillham to be identified
as the author of the Work has been asserted by him in
accordance with the Copyright, Designs and Patents Act 1988.

Published by Hodder Children's Books 1995

Copyright © WEC Gillham 1983

10 9 8 7 6 5 4

All rights reserved. No part of this publication may be reproduced, stored
in a retrieval system, or transmitted, in any form or by any means,
without the prior written permission of the publisher, nor be otherwise
circulated in any form of binding or cover other than that in which it is
published and without a similar condition being imposed on the
subsequent purchaser.

ISBN 0 340 651105

Printed and bound in Great Britain

Hodder Children's Books
A division of Hodder Headline plc
338 Euston Road
London NW1 3BH

Previously published as Test Your Child's Mental Arithmetic

The answer goes in the box

1A

1 Add 3 and 4.

2 Take 4 away from 10.

3 3 x 5 =

4 How many twos in eight?

5 How many pence make a pound?

6 If your football team scores five goals in the first half and two in the second half, how many does it score altogether?

7 If you have nine marbles and you lose three of them, how many do you have left?

8 If three children get four biscuits each, how many biscuits do they have altogether?

9 If ten sweets are shared between five children, how many do they get each?

10 If you have two 50p pieces and a 20p piece, how many pounds and pence is that altogether?

11 You get three library books from the library every week. How many library books do you read in a month?

12 If you have five apples and you eat them all, how many do you have left?

13 If eleven people eat two sandwiches each, how many were there to begin with?

14 If you have ten small cakes, how many people can have three each?

15 In your money box there are 200 pennies. How much is that in pounds?

The grown-up rings √ if the answer is right, ✗ if it is nearly right and × if it is wrong.

score

15

No working out on paper
1B

1 Add 5 and 3. ☐ ✓ ✗ ✗

2 Take 5 away from 11. ☐ ✓ ✗ ✗

3 4 x 4 = ☐ ✓ ✗ ✗

4 How many threes in nine? ☐ ✓ ✗ ✗

5 What is half of ten? ☐ ✓ ✗ ✗

6 What is 235p in pounds and pence? ☐ ✓ ✗ ✗

7 If there are five chairs in one room, two in another and six in another, how many are there altogether? ☐ ✓ ✗ ✗

8 If twelve children are invited to a party and three can't come, how many come to the party? ☐ ✓ ✗ ✗

9 If there are six boxes with three pencils in each, how many pencils are there altogether? ☐ ✓ ✗ ✗

10 If a caterpillar has twenty feet, how many pairs of shoes will he need? ☐ ✓ ✗ ✗

11 If your teacher has sixteen pencils and half of them get broken, how many are left? ☐ ✓ ✗ ✗

12 You have two 20p pieces and one 10p piece. How much more do you need to make a pound? ☐ ✓ ✗ ✗

13 If four stamps of the same value cost £1, how much did they cost each? ☐ ✓ ✗ ✗

14 If you have fifteen marbles, buy four more and then lose two, how many are you left with? ☐ ✓ ✗ ✗

15 In a class of 24 children there are only six rubbers. How many children have to share one rubber? ☐ ✓ ✗ ✗

Write down the answer only

☐ score

| 15 |

Work it out in your head
1C

1 Add 6 and 9.

2 Take 8 away from 13.

3 5 x 5 =

4 How many fours in twenty?

5 What is half of 24?

6 What is 10p less than £1?

7 If the postman delivers five letters on Monday, five on Wednesday and eight on Friday, how many letters is that altogether?

8 If there are 15 boys in a class of 28 children, how many are girls?

9 For every job you do in the house you are given 40p. If you do four jobs how much do you earn?

10 One big cake is cut into quarters. How many pieces are there?

11 Going past in a train you count the legs of the sheep in a field. There are 40 legs. How many sheep are there?

12 You buy a model plane kit for £2.80. Next time you go to the shop the kits have gone up by 20p. How much does one cost now?

13 If you buy two chocolate bars for 70p, how much change do you have from £1?

14 If there are six cakes and twelve children, how much do they get each?

15 You ask your mother for 50p, but she says she will give you only half that. How much do you get?

A near miss scores half a point

score

15

5

The check test is an oral test

1D Check Test

The adult asks the questions, the child gives the answers.
Any mistakes should be followed up.

1 Add 6 and 9.

2 Take 5 away from 11.

3 4 x 4 =

4 How many twos in eight?

5 What is half of 24?

6 If your football team scores five goals in the first half and two in the second half, how many does it score altogether?

7 If there are five chairs in one room, two in another and six in another, how many are there altogether?

8 If three children get four biscuits each, how many biscuits do they have altogether?

9 For every job you do in the house you are given 40p. If you do four jobs how much do you earn?

10 If you have two 50p pieces and a 20p piece, how many pounds and pence is that altogether?

11 If your teacher has sixteen pencils and half of them get broken, how many are left?

12 You buy a model plane kit for £2.80. Next time you go to the shop the kits have gone up by 20p. How much does one cost now?

13 If four stamps of the same value cost £1, how much did they cost each?

14 If you have ten small cakes, how many people can have three each?

15 You ask your mother for 50p, but she says she will give you only half that. How much do you get?

No pencil needed for the check test

A good guess is better than nothing

2A

GUESS!

1 Add 6 and 3 and 4.

2 Take 8 away from 17.

3 4 x 6 =

4 How many sevens in twenty-one?

5 What is quarter of forty?

6 What is 15p more than 90p?

7 Shooting a rifle at the funfair you score
six, two, a miss and three. What is your
total score?

8 If you get $^7/_{10}$, $^8/_{10}$ and $^5/_{10}$ in three spelling tests,
how many spellings did you get wrong altogether?

9 With each packet of cornflakes there is a 10p
token. How much do you have in tokens from
five packets?

10 You have twelve sweets but you give a quarter
of them to your sister. How many does she get?

11 On craft afternoon your teacher asks you to
give out 3 paint pots to each child in the class
who is doing painting. You give out 18 pots.
How many children are doing painting?

12 What is 50p less than £1.25?

13 If you buy three sticks of bubble-gum at 10p
each, how much change do you have from 50p?

14 If there are three cakes and twelve children,
how much do they get each?

15 When you go to the library you expect the fine
on your book to be 25p but it costs three times
as much. How much does it cost?

Read the questions carefully

score

15

Don't use your fingers – use your head

2B

1 Add 5 and 6 and 7.

2 Take 6 away from 15.

3 $4 \times 7 =$

4 How many sixes in thirty-six?

5 What is a quarter of twenty-four?

6 What is 20p less than £1.10?

7 Playing cricket you score a six and two fours before being clean bowled. What is your total score?

8 You buy a model plane kit which should have 24 parts, but 5 are missing. How many pieces are you left with?

9 You are saving 5p pieces in a tin. When you count them you have eighteen. How much is that altogether?

10 It is Bonfire Night and you have let off half your fireworks. You have nine left. How many did you start with?

11 You have 25 sheets of paper and you have to give out 3 to each child in your class. If you have one left over how many children have you given paper to?

12 If you have a quarter of an hour for playtime, how many minutes is that?

13 If you buy two comics that cost the same and you have 20p change from £1, how much did the comics cost *each*?

14 Your mother gives you six chocolate biscuits to share with your brother. If you eat twice as many as he does, how many does he get?

15 You get $^{10}/_{20}$ in a maths test but the boy next to you in class gets half as much again. What is his mark?

Use your pencil only for writing the answer

8

score

15

Keep your brain dusted!

2C

1 Add 3 and 0 and 9.

2 Take 8 away from 13.

3 $8 \times 2 =$

4 How many fours in forty-eight?

5 What is half of forty-four?

6 What is 30p less than £1.20?

7 You have seven pieces of red Lego and four pieces of blue Lego. Your friend gives you five more pieces of red Lego and six more pieces of blue Lego. How much do you have of the two colours now? (Give two answers please)

8 You have bought a giant set of 30 felt-tip pens. You lose three at school and lend four to a friend. How many do you have left?

9 When you ask your mother for some money, she gives you all the coins in her purse. There are four 20p pieces and four 5p pieces. How much do you get?

10 If you have an hour for lunch at school and it takes you 10 minutes to eat your dinner, how long do you have to play?

11 At a party you play a game where you are blindfolded, given a pack of 36 cards and told to walk round a circle of children giving one card to each child. When you have gone round the circle three times there are no cards left. How many children were there?

12 What is 21p more than £1.80?

13 You buy three rockets for Bonfire Night. From a five pound note you get a 20p piece, two 10p pieces, and two 5p pieces in change. How much did the rockets cost each?

14 If six children get half a chocolate bar each and two children get a whole one each, how many chocolate bars were there to start with?

15 If you are ten years old and your mother is three times as old as you, how old is she?

Write down the answer only

score

15

9

The check test is an oral test

2D Check Test

The adult asks the questions, the child gives the answers.
Any mistakes should be followed up.

1 Add 3 and 0 and 9.

2 Take 6 away from 15.

3 $4 \times 7 =$

4 How many sevens in twenty-one?

5 What is half of forty-four?

6 What is 15p more than 90p?

7 Playing cricket you score a six and two fours before being clean bowled. What is your total score?

8 If you get $7/10$, $8/10$ and $5/10$ in three spelling tests, how many spellings did you get wrong altogether?

9 When you ask your mother for some money she gives you all the coins in her purse. There are four 20p pieces and four 5p pieces. How much do you get?

10 You have twelve sweets but you give a quarter of them to your sister. How many does she get?

11 You have 25 sheets of paper and you have to give out 3 to each child in your class. If you have one left over how many children have you given paper to?

12 What is 21p more than £1.80?

13 If you buy two comics that cost the same and you have 20p change from £1, how much did the comics cost *each*?

14 If there are three cakes and twelve children, how much do they get each?

15 If you are ten years old and your mother is three times as old as you, how old is she?

No pencil needed for the check test

Your brain is the best calculator – it needs no batteries!

3A

1 Add 1 and 2 and 3 and 4. ☐ ✓ ✗ ✗

2 Take 6 away from 11. ☐ ✓ ✗ ✗

3 5 x 7 = ☐ ✓ ✗ ✗

4 How many fours in sixteen? ☐ ✓ ✗ ✗

5 How much is £10 and £18 and £12? ☐ ✓ ✗ ✗

6 How many millimetres in two centimetres? ☐ ✓ ✗ ✗

7 How many minutes in two hours? ☐ ✓ ✗ ✗

8 You are playing cards and turn up a six, a three and a four; your sister turns up a seven, a four and a five. Who wins, and by how much? ☐ ✓ ✗ ✗

9 If the minute hand of a clock goes half-way round the dial, how many minutes is that? ☐ ✓ ✗ ✗

10 If you save £1 a week, how long will it take you to save £18? ☐ ✓ ✗ ✗

11 If a car is travelling at 60 kilometres per hour (k.p.h.) how far will it travel in one and a half hours? ☐ ✓ ✗ ✗

12 If you and your two friends have £1.20 between you and you both have the same amount, how much do you have each? ☐ ✓ ✗ ✗

13 In your stamp collection you only need 15 more stamps to have 100 different French stamps. How many French stamps do you have at the moment? ☐ ✓ ✗ ✗

14 You have fifty marbles. Your brother has ten fewer marbles than you, and your sister has ten fewer than your brother. How many marbles does your sister have? ☐ ✓ ✗ ✗

15 A snail moves 10 centimetres in 10 minutes. How long will it take to cover a metre? ☐ ✓ ✗ ✗

Always check your answers

☐ score

| 15 |

11

Working out on the back of your hand is not allowed

3B

1 Add 3 and 4 and 5.

2 Take 7 away from 12.

3 9 x 3 =

4 How many eights in forty?

5 How much is £7 and £8 and £15?

6 How many centimetres in two metres?

7 How many minutes in an hour and a quarter?

8 You roll a pair of dice. The first time you get a six and a two, the next time a five and a four. What is the difference?

9 If the minute hand of a clock goes one and a half times round the dial, how many minutes is that?

10 You have put 50p a week in your money box, and now you have saved £7.50. How many weeks have you been saving?

11 If the driver of a car travelling at 60 k.p.h. stops for a ten-minute break every hour, how far does he travel in two hours?

12 Your uncle leaves £10 to be divided equally between you and your three brothers. How much do you get?

13 You have 35 CDs, your friend has 17 more than you. How many does he have?

14 You start with 60 sweets. You eat half on the first day and then eat half of the remainder on the second day. How many do you have left?

15 The sea is washing away a cliff at the rate of 3 metres a year. The front of a holiday bungalow is 12 metres from the cliff edge. In how many years will the front door be at the cliff edge?

Think before you write!

score

15

12

When in doubt – guess!
3C

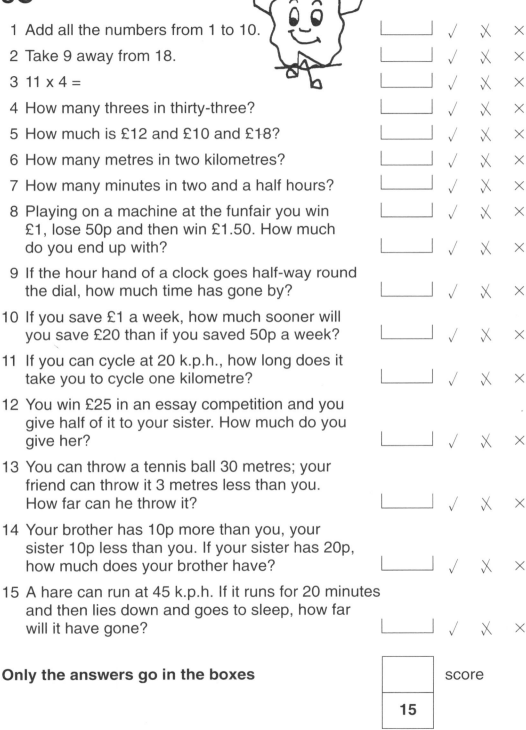

GUESS!

1 Add all the numbers from 1 to 10.

2 Take 9 away from 18.

3 11 x 4 =

4 How many threes in thirty-three?

5 How much is £12 and £10 and £18?

6 How many metres in two kilometres?

7 How many minutes in two and a half hours?

8 Playing on a machine at the funfair you win £1, lose 50p and then win £1.50. How much do you end up with?

9 If the hour hand of a clock goes half-way round the dial, how much time has gone by?

10 If you save £1 a week, how much sooner will you save £20 than if you saved 50p a week?

11 If you can cycle at 20 k.p.h., how long does it take you to cycle one kilometre?

12 You win £25 in an essay competition and you give half of it to your sister. How much do you give her?

13 You can throw a tennis ball 30 metres; your friend can throw it 3 metres less than you. How far can he throw it?

14 Your brother has 10p more than you, your sister 10p less than you. If your sister has 20p, how much does your brother have?

15 A hare can run at 45 k.p.h. If it runs for 20 minutes and then lies down and goes to sleep, how far will it have gone?

Only the answers go in the boxes

score

15

13

The check test is an oral test

3D Check Test

The adult asks the questions, the child gives the answers.
Any mistakes should be followed up.

1 Add all the numbers from 1 to 10.

2 Take 7 away from 12.

3 9 x 3 =

4 How many fours in sixteen?

5 How many threes in thirty-three?

6 How many millimetres in two centimetres?

7 How many minutes in an hour and a quarter?

8 You are playing cards and turn up a six, a three and a four; your sister turns up a seven, a four and a five. Who wins, and by how much?

9 If the hour hand of a clock goes half-way round the dial, how much time has gone by?

10 If you save £1 a week, how much sooner will you save £20 than if you saved 50p a week?

11 If the driver of a car travelling at 60 k.p.h. stops for a ten-minute break every hour, how far does he travel in two hours?

12 You win £25 in an essay competition and you give half of it to your sister. How much do you give her?

13 You have 35 CDs, your friend has 17 more than you. How many does he have?

14 You have fifty marbles, your brother has ten fewer than you, and your sister has ten fewer than your brother. How many marbles does your sister have?

15 A hare can run at 45 k.p.h. If it runs for 20 minutes and then lies down and goes to sleep, how far will it have gone?

No pencil needed for the check test

Concentrate!

4A

1 Add 17 and 6.

2 Take 8 away from 15.

3 5 x 8 =

4 How many sixes in eighteen?

5 How much is 65p and 45p?

6 How many metres in half a kilometre?

7 If you leave home at eight o'clock and arrive at school at quarter to nine, how long has it taken you?

8 A darts player scores 2, 16 and 14 with three darts. What is his total score?

9 You go to sleep at nine o'clock every night and wake up at seven in the morning. How long are you asleep?

10 For your holiday you save £5 a month for six months. How much do you save?

11 If you can do 100 skips in 3 minutes, how long does it take you to do 50 skips?

12 You have seen two purple cars today, yesterday you saw twice as many. How many purple cars have you seen in the two days?

13 When you look in your box of marbles you find 15 marbles, 8 fewer than you expected. How many did you expect to find?

14 Today you scored 18 out of 20 in a spelling test, 5 more than yesterday. How many did you score yesterday?

15 You measure your thumb-nail and it is $1\frac{1}{2}$ centimetres long. How many millimetres is that?

score

15

You'd be lost without a brain!

Better a nearly-right answer than no answer at all

4B

1 Add 18 and 9. ☐ ✓ ✗ ✗

2 Take 9 away from 21. ☐ ✓ ✗ ✗

3 5 x 6 = ☐ ✓ ✗ ✗

4 How many threes in twenty-one? ☐ ✓ ✗ ✗

5 How much is £14, £7 and £2? ☐ ✓ ✗ ✗

6 How many centimetres in half a metre? ☐ ✓ ✗ ✗

7 If the train leaves your local station at a quarter past two and reaches London two hours later, at what time does it arrive? ☐ ✓ ✗ ✗

8 On a computer game you score two twenties and a fifteen. What is your total score? ☐ ✓ ✗ ✗

9 If you go to bed every night at the same time and sleep ten hours, how many hours are you awake during the day? ☐ ✓ ✗ ✗

10 If it is 500 metres round the race track, how many times do you go round for 1 kilometre? ☐ ✓ ✗ ✗

11 You have found twenty conkers, four times as many as last week. How many did you find last week? ☐ ✓ ✗ ✗

12 There are twenty pears on your tree this year, twelve fewer than last year. How many were there last year? ☐ ✓ ✗ ✗

13 Your bus fare cost you £2.25, 50p more than you expected. How much did you expect it would cost? ☐ ✓ ✗ ✗

14 If you are 1$\frac{1}{2}$ metres tall, how many centimetres is that? ☐ ✓ ✗ ✗

15 If a cake is cut into quarters and then each quarter is cut in half, how many pieces is that? ☐ ✓ ✗ ✗

☐ score

The check-list makes sure you know it

15

Practice makes you quicker

4C

1 Add 21 and 11.

2 Take 12 away from 27.

3 $9 \times 2 =$

4 How many fives in forty?

5 How much is £7, £8 and £15?

6 How many millimetres in half a centimetre?

7 At the beginning of the year there were 32 children in your class. Later on, 5 left, but 3 new children have come in. How many children are there in the class now?

8 Playing cricket you score a four in each of three overs, and then a six in the fourth over before being caught out. How many did you score altogether?

9 Your mother can get to work in 15 minutes in the morning, but coming home in the rush hour takes three times as long. How long does the return journey take?

10 If a car is going at 60 kilometres an hour, how far does it go in one minute?

11 Your weekly pocket money is £1.50, three times as much as last year. How much was it last year?

12 If a square room has walls each three metres long, how far is it all the way round the room?

13 If your school starts at nine o'clock and finishes at four o'clock, how many hours are you at school if you don't go home to lunch?

14 If a car's petrol tank holds seventy litres and it is half full, how much petrol is there in the tank?

15 Your grandfather gives you £10 for your savings account, doubling the amount you have in it. How much did you have before?

Simple sums are best done in your head

score

15

17

The check test is an oral test

4D Check Test

The adult asks the questions, the child gives the answers.
Any mistakes should be followed up.

1 Add 21 and 11.

2 Take 9 away from 21.

3 5 x 6 =

4 How many sixes in eighteen?

5 How much is £7, £8 and £15?

6 How many metres in half a kilometre?

7 If the train leaves your local station at a quarter past two and reaches London two hours later, at what time does it arrive?

8 A darts player scores 2, 16 and 14 with three darts. What is his total score?

9 Your mother can get to work in 15 minutes in the morning, but coming home in the rush hour takes three times as long. How long does the return journey take?

10 For your holiday you save £5 a month for six months. How much do you save?

11 You have found twenty conkers, four times as many as last week. How many did you find last week?

12 If a square room has walls each three metres long, how far is it all the way round the room?

13 Your bus fare cost you £2.25, 50p more than you expected. How much did you expect it would cost?

14 Today you scored 18 out of 20 in a spelling test, 5 more than yesterday. How many did you score yesterday?

15 Your grandfather gives you £10 for your savings account, doubling the amount you have in it. How much did you have before?

No pencil needed for the check test

Remember – you won't always have a calculator handy!

5A

1 Add 27 and 18. ☐ ✓ ✗ ✗

2 Take 17 away from 32. ☐ ✓ ✗ ✗

3 6 x 9 = ☐ ✓ ✗ ✗

4 How many sixes in forty-eight? ☐ ✓ ✗ ✗

5 How much is £1.25 and £1.27? ☐ ✓ ✗ ✗

6 How many millimetres in 2$\frac{1}{2}$ centimetres? ☐ ✓ ✗ ✗

7 If you start with 20 marbles, lose 9 and then win 12, how many do you end up with? ☐ ✓ ✗ ✗

8 If there are ten one-litre lemonade bottles but half of them are only half full, how many litres are left to drink? ☐ ✓ ✗ ✗

9 When your father pays for the groceries at the supermarket check-out, he gets £1.73 change from a £10 note. How much did the groceries cost? ☐ ✓ ✗ ✗

10 If a kilogramme of biscuits is divided equally into two bags, how many grammes are there in each bag? ☐ ✓ ✗ ✗

11 You are 1 metre 53 cm tall, 13 cm taller than your brother. How tall is he? ☐ ✓ ✗ ✗

12 Your mother puts a pie in the oven at half past five. If it takes an hour and a quarter to cook, at what time will it be ready? ☐ ✓ ✗ ✗

13 Your white mouse is in a square cage, each side of which is 50 cm long. If he runs all the way round the edge just once, how far does he run? ☐ ✓ ✗ ✗

14 You have 50 g of small sweets and you have to make up paper bags of 5 g each. How many bags of sweets will there be? ☐ ✓ ✗ ✗

15 If $\frac{3}{4}$ kg of biscuits costs £1.50 how much will a kilogramme cost? ☐ ✓ ✗ ✗

Learn to do it in your head!

score

15

If you want a rough guess round up or down to the nearest 10

5B

1 Add 19 and 31. ⌣ ✓ ✗ ✗

2 Take 19 away from 31. ⌣ ✓ ✗ ✗

3 7 x 8 = ⌣ ✓ ✗ ✗

4 How many eights in fifty-six? ⌣ ✓ ✗ ✗

5 How much is £1.07 and £2.35? ⌣ ✓ ✗ ✗

6 How many metres in 2¹/₂ kilometres? ⌣ ✓ ✗ ✗

7 Take 20 paces forwards, 2 backwards and then 13 paces forwards. How many paces forward are you from where you started? ⌣ ✓ ✗ ✗

8 If a car does ten kilometres to a litre of petrol, how many litres has it used up in 30 kilometres? ⌣ ✓ ✗ ✗

9 Your father buys butter at 82p, sugar at 68p and eggs at 73p. Round up or down to the nearest 10p. What is the total cost worked out in this way? ⌣ ✓ ✗ ✗

10 If 8 children (a ¹/₄ of the class) are off sick, how many children are there in the class usually? ⌣ ✓ ✗ ✗

11 You are half-way to school when you realize that you will be late if you don't run. You run twice as fast as you walk and you get there in five minutes. How long does it take you to do the *whole* journey *walking*? ⌣ ✓ ✗ ✗

12 You get ¹⁶/₂₀ for a spelling test. Your friend gets only three-quarters as many marks as you. How many does *he* get out of twenty? ⌣ ✓ ✗ ✗

13 If cooking apples weigh 100 g each, how many would you get in a kilogramme? ⌣ ✓ ✗ ✗

14 If your sister gets £4 a week pocket money, you get half of that, and your brother gets half as much as you – how much does he get? ⌣ ✓ ✗ ✗

15 If a train leaving at three o'clock is a quarter of an hour late on a journey that should take only an hour, at what time does it arrive? ⌣ ✓ ✗ ✗

How to round up or down to the nearest 10p:
50p, 51p, 52p, 53p, 54p all become 50p.
55p, 56p, 57p, 58p, 59p all become 60p, and so on.
Remember 5 rounds upwards.

	score
15	

The brain – man's first computer

5C

1 Add 27 and 25.

2 Take 27 away from 45.

3 10 x 9 =

4 How many elevens in seventy-seven?

5 How much is £3.70 and £1.35?

6 How many centimetres in 3½ metres?

7 If you start with £5, spend 60p on sweets, 40p on a comic, and then earn 50p for running an errand, how much do you end up with?

8 If a bus leaves at 13.00 hours on the 24-hour clock and arrives half an hour later, what is the time of arrival on the 12-hour clock?

9 You weigh 25 kilos, 500 grammes more than you did six months ago. How much did you weigh then?

10 If a car is travelling at 60 km an hour, how far does it travel in 30 seconds?

11 If a cake is cut into quarters, and then each piece is cut into quarters again, how many pieces are there?

12 There are three trees: one is 31 metres tall, one is 21 metres tall. The height of the third one is half-way between the other two. How tall is it?

13 David has 20 marbles, Andrew has twice as many but Richard has only a quarter of what Andrew has. How many marbles has Richard got?

14 If your little sister's bricks are 10 centimetres high, how many will she need to build a tower 1½ metres high?

15 If you buy two chocolate bars at 35p each, how much change will you have from £1?

Learn how to program your brain!

score

15

21

The check test is an oral test

5D Check Test

The adult asks the questions, the child gives the answers.
Any mistakes should be followed up.

1 Add 27 and 25.

2 Take 19 away from 31.

3 $7 \times 8 =$

4 How many sixes in forty-eight?

5 How much is £3.70 and £1.35?

6 How many millimetres in $2\frac{1}{2}$ centimetres?

7 Take 20 paces forwards, 2 backwards and then 13 paces forwards. How many paces forward are you from where you started?

8 If there are ten one-litre lemonade bottles but half of them are only half full, how many litres are left to drink?

9 You weigh 25 kilos, 500 grammes more than you did six months ago How much did you weigh then?

10 If a kilogramme of biscuits is divided equally into two bags, how many grammes are there in each bag?

11 You are half-way to school when you realize that you will be late if you don't run. You run twice as fast as you walk and you get there in five minutes. How long does it take you to do the *whole* journey *walking*?

12 There are three trees: one is 31 metres tall, one is 21 metres tall. The height of the third one is half-way between the other two. How tall is it?

13 If cooking apples weigh 100 g each, how many would you get in a kilogramme?

14 You have 50 g of small sweets and you have to make up paper bags of 5 g each. How many bags of sweets will there be?

15 If you buy two chocolate bars at 35p each, how much change will you have from £1?

No pencil needed for the check test

22

Always look for a short cut
6A

1 Add 17 and 15 and 13.

2 Add 15 and 35 and then take away 12.

3 3 x 3 x 3 =

4 How many nines in eighty-one?

5 Take 80p away from £2.00.

6 Add 1¹/₂ metres and 50 centimetres.

7 What is a third of 90?

8 How long is one side of a square metre?

9 These numbers make a pattern. What would
   the next number be? 12, 20, 28, 36, ...

10 Two cars set out at the same time to a town
   80 kilometres away. One car travels at 80
   kilometres per hour, the other at 40 kilometres
   per hour. How much longer does the slower
   car take?

11 What is 10% of £100?

12 A leather football costs £40. A good plastic one
   costs half as much and the cheapest one costs
   a *quarter of that*. How much is the cheapest one?

13 You are going to see a film which starts at 7 pm
   and finishes at 9.30 pm. What are the times of
   starting and finishing on the 24-hour clock?

14 If you were born on the 21st January 1985, how
   old would you be on the 18th June 1995 in years
   and completed months?

15 If your parents buy six 3-metre floorboards at £4
   a metre, how much do they cost?

Use your brain to save your brain

score

15

There may be an easy way and a hard way. Think …

6B

1 Add 19 and 12 and 30.

2 Add 30 and 15 and then take away 14.

3 4 x 4 x 2 =

4 How many twelves in seventy-two?

5 Take 75p away from £2.50.

6 Add 3¹/₂ centimetres and 5 millimetres.

7 What is a quarter of 120?

8 How long is one side of a square kilometre?

9 In a supermarket you buy a tin of beans at 47p, a packet of bacon at £1.23 and a packet of tea-bags at 93p. Rounding up or down to the nearest 10p, what is the 'guess' price altogether?

10 On your new bicycle you can travel at 30 kilometres per hour. How long does it take you to get to your school 3 kilometres away?

11 What is 10% of £10?

12 These numbers make a pattern. What would the next number be?
601, 701, 801, 901, ...

13 Your father says he will pay you 20p for every bag of grass cuttings you collect, and 10p bonus for every six bags. You fill 18 bags. How much do you earn?

14 If the 20th September is a Monday, what day of the week will 4th October be?

15 A 1 kg box of cornflakes costs £1.80. A 500 g box costs £1.05. How much do you save in the long term by buying the kilo box?

Rounding makes it easier to add up several small amounts with near-miss accuracy

score

15

24

Using your brain makes life easier

6C

1 Add 38 and 18 and 33. ☐ ✓ ✗ ✗

2 Add 17 and 47 and then halve the total. ☐ ✓ ✗ ✗

3 2 x 10 x 4 = ☐ ✓ ✗ ✗

4 How many twelves in one hundred and twenty? ☐ ✓ ✗ ✗

5 Take £1.28 away from £4.33. ☐ ✓ ✗ ✗

6 If three boys are 1 m 50 cm, 1 m 60cm and 1 m 70 cm tall, what is their average height? ☐ ✓ ✗ ✗

7 What is a third of 180? ☐ ✓ ✗ ✗

8 If a table is 1 metre long and 2 metres wide, how far is it round the edge (the *perimeter*)? ☐ ✓ ✗ ✗

9 Your mother hires a rowing boat to go on the lake in the public park. It costs £4 for the first hour then 50p for each 10 minutes after that. You return the boat after 1½ hours. How much does it cost your mother? ☐ ✓ ✗ ✗

10 In a litre bottle of cola there is only 125 ml (millilitres) left. How much has been drunk (in millilitres)? ☐ ✓ ✗ ✗

11 What is one quarter expressed as a decimal? ☐ ✓ ✗ ✗

12 Your father wants to tile the top of a coffee table measuring 40 cm by 80 cm. The tiles are 10cm square. How many will he need? ☐ ✓ ✗ ✗

13 These numbers make a pattern. What would the next number be? 14, 18, 22, 26, ... ☐ ✓ ✗ ✗

14 A kilo of biscuits costs only £2.40 because you get 250 g free. What would it cost to buy just 250 g of biscuits at the normal price? ☐ ✓ ✗ ✗

15 You have saved up to buy a mountain bike which cost £200 when you first saw it. But the price has increased by 10%. How much does it cost now? ☐ ✓ ✗ ✗

☐ score

15

There is no substitute for your brain

The check test is an oral test

6D Check Test

The adult asks the questions, the child gives the answers.
Any mistakes should be followed up.

1 Add 38 and 18 and 33.

2 Add 30 and 15 and then take away 14.

3 4 x 4 x 2 =

4 How many nines in eighty-one?

5 Take £1.28 away from £4.33.

6 Add 1$^1/_2$ metres and 50 centimetres.

7 What is a quarter of 120?

8 How long is one side of a square metre?

9 Your mother hires a rowing boat to go on the lake in the public park. It costs £4 for the first hour then 50p for each 10 minutes after that. You return the boat after 1$^1/_2$ hours. How much does it cost your mother?

10 Two cars set out at the same time to a town 80 kilometres away. One car travels at 80 kilometres per hour, the other at 40 kilometres per hour. How much longer does the slower car take?

11 What is 10% of £10?

12 Your father wants to tile the top of a coffee table measuring 40 cm by 80 cm. The tiles are 10 cm square. How many will he need?

13 Your father says he will pay you 20p for every bag of grass cuttings you collect, and 10p bonus for every six bags. You fill 18 bags. How much do you earn?

14 If you were born on the 21st January 1985, how old would you be on the 18th June 1995 in years and completed months?

15 You have saved up to buy a mountain bike which cost £200 when you first saw it. But the price has increased by 10%. How much does it cost now?

No pencil needed for the check test

Can you think for yourself?

7A

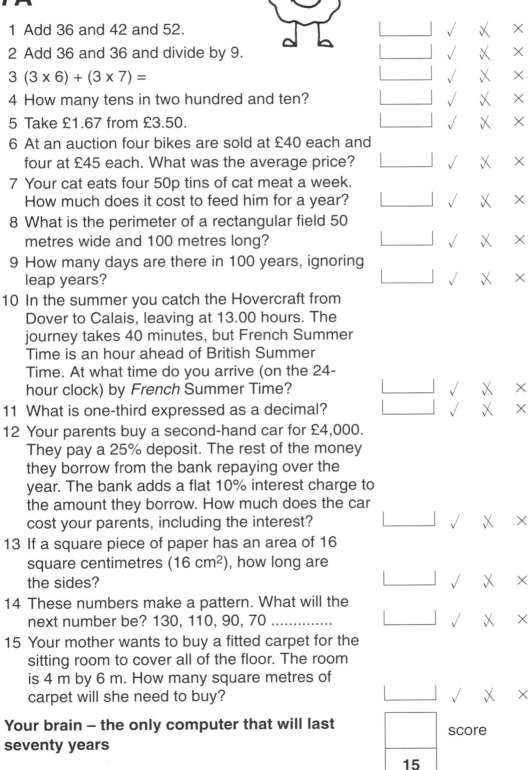

1 Add 36 and 42 and 52.

2 Add 36 and 36 and divide by 9.

3 (3 x 6) + (3 x 7) =

4 How many tens in two hundred and ten?

5 Take £1.67 from £3.50.

6 At an auction four bikes are sold at £40 each and four at £45 each. What was the average price?

7 Your cat eats four 50p tins of cat meat a week. How much does it cost to feed him for a year?

8 What is the perimeter of a rectangular field 50 metres wide and 100 metres long?

9 How many days are there in 100 years, ignoring leap years?

10 In the summer you catch the Hovercraft from Dover to Calais, leaving at 13.00 hours. The journey takes 40 minutes, but French Summer Time is an hour ahead of British Summer Time. At what time do you arrive (on the 24-hour clock) by *French* Summer Time?

11 What is one-third expressed as a decimal?

12 Your parents buy a second-hand car for £4,000. They pay a 25% deposit. The rest of the money they borrow from the bank repaying over the year. The bank adds a flat 10% interest charge to the amount they borrow. How much does the car cost your parents, including the interest?

13 If a square piece of paper has an area of 16 square centimetres (16 cm^2), how long are the sides?

14 These numbers make a pattern. What will the next number be? 130, 110, 90, 70 ....

15 Your mother wants to buy a fitted carpet for the sitting room to cover all of the floor. The room is 4 m by 6 m. How many square metres of carpet will she need to buy?

Your brain – the only computer that will last seventy years

score

15

27

You won't always have a calculator, but you're never without your head

7B

1 Add 51 and 23 and 38.

2 Add 45 and 39 and divide by 7.

3 (4 x 8) + (9 x 5) =

4 How many nines in nine hundred and nine?

5 Take £3.82 from £4.97.

6 The rainfall for one week is 13 mm on Sunday, nothing on Monday and Tuesday, 7 mm on Wednesday, 10 mm on Thursday, 1 mm on Friday and 4 mm on Saturday. What was the *average* in millimetres for the seven days?

7 What is three-quarters of forty-eight?

8 You have to cut 6 cm rods from a steel rod 50 cm in length. How many rods can you cut?

9 You take two books out from the library on the 17th July but don't return them until the 21st August. If you don't take them back after two weeks, you pay a fine of 20p for the first week and 30p a week after that. How much do you have to pay in fines?

10 If a football match lasts 45 minutes each way, with a 15-minute interval and 10 minutes extra for injuries that held up the game, how long did the game last from start to finish?

11 What is $1\frac{1}{2}$ expressed as a decimal?

12 You give 20p for a poppy on Remembrance Day; your father gives two and a half times as much. How much does he give?

13 If a square piece of paper has an area of 25 square centimetres, what are the lengths of the sides?

14 If firemen are pumping water from a 10,000-litre tank at the rate of 250 litres a minute, how long will the supply last?

15 These numbers make a pattern. What will the next number be? 36, 49, 64, 81 ....

Watch it! Some of these are easy to get right – and easy to get wrong!

28

score

15

If you've got this far, your brain's in better shape

7C

1 Add 72 and 15 and 28. ☐ ✓ ✗ ✗

2 Add 62 and 59 and divide by 11. ☐ ✓ ✗ ✗

3 $(6 \times 6) + (7 \times 7) =$ ☐ ✓ ✗ ✗

4 How many twenty-ones in a hundred and sixty-eight? ☐ ✓ ✗ ✗

5 Take £7.34 from £9.09. ☐ ✓ ✗ ✗

6 Your batting average for the last season was 32. This season you have scored 28, 63, 42 and 35. How much better is your average so far this season? ☐ ✓ ✗ ✗

7 What is one-fifth of a hundred? ☐ ✓ ✗ ✗

8 How many pieces 10 cm x 5 cm can you cut out of a piece of wood 1 metre long and 50 cm wide? ☐ ✓ ✗ ✗

9 If you wind up an eight-day clock on the 1st January, how many times will you have had to wind it up by the 2nd March in a leap year? ☐ ✓ ✗ ✗

10 If a 3-kilowatt electric fire costs 8p per hour per kilowatt, how much does it cost to run it for 30 minutes? ☐ ✓ ✗ ✗

11 What is $8^{3}/_{4}$ expressed as a decimal? ☐ ✓ ✗ ✗

12 If a rectangular room is 4 metres wide and 5 metres long, how many square metres of carpet will you need to cover half of the floor area? ☐ ✓ ✗ ✗

13 These numbers make a pattern. What would the next number be? 1, 3, 6, 10 .... ☐ ✓ ✗ ✗

14 A baby was born on September 22nd, seventeen days earlier than expected. What date was he expected to be born on? ☐ ✓ ✗ ✗

15 Petrol costs 60p a litre and a car does 5 kilometres to the litre in town, 6 kilometres to the litre on the motorway. What is the difference in cost between doing a kilometre in town and doing a kilometre on the motorway? ☐ ✓ ✗ ✗

Brains need exercise too!

score

15

29

The check test is an oral test

7D Check Test

The adult asks the questions, the child gives the answers.
Any mistakes should be followed up.

1 Add 72 and 15 and 28.

2 Add 45 and 39 and divide by 7.

3 (4 x 8) + (9 x 5) =

4 How many tens in two hundred and ten?

5 Take £7.34 from £9.09.

6 At an auction four bikes are sold at £40 each and four at £45 each. What was the average price?

7 What is three-quarters of forty-eight?

8 What is the perimeter of a rectangular field 50 metres wide and 100 metres long?

9 If you wind up an eight-day clock on the 1st January, how many times will you have had to wind it up by the 2nd March in a leap year?

10 In the summer you catch the Hovercraft from Dover to Calais, leaving at 13.00 hours. The journey takes 40 minutes, but French Summer Time is an hour ahead of British Summer Time. At what time do you arrive (on the 24-hour clock) by *French* Summer Time?

11 What is $1\frac{1}{2}$ expressed as a decimal?

12 If a rectangular room is 4 metres wide and 5 metres long, how many square metres of carpet will you need to cover half of the floor area?

13 If a square piece of paper has an area of 25 square centimetres, what are the lengths of the sides?

14 These numbers make a pattern. What will the next number be?
130, 110, 90, 70 ....

15 Petrol costs 60p a litre and a car does 5 kilometres to the litre in town, 6 kilometres to the litre on the motorway. What is the difference in cost between doing a kilometre in town and doing a kilometre on the motorway?

No pencil needed for the check test

You do this on your own!

End-of-Book Test

1 Add 17 and 14.

2 Add 15 and 20 and 25.

3 Take 11 away from 30.

4 Add 28 and 14 and then take away 19.

5 7 x 6 =

6 How many eights in four hundred?

7 How many twenty-fives in two hundred and fifty?

8 What is 65p more than £1.90?

9 Take £2.37 away from £7.18.

10 How many millimetres in 17.5 centimetres?

11 Add $1^1/4$ metres and 37 centimetres.

12 What is an eighth of 16?

13 What is a twenty-fifth of 125?

14 If an athlete wins the 5000-metre race in 25 minutes, what is her speed in kilometres per hour?

15 You buy a drawing book at 99p, a stencil at 75p and a pencil at 42p. Rounding up or down to the nearest 10p, what is your guess-estimate total cost?

16 What is $12^1/2$% of £100?

17 Two cars set out for a town 100 kilometres away. The first car (A) travels at 60 k.p.h. The second car (B) leaves half an hour later but travels at 90 k.p.h. Which car gets there first – A or B?

18 The sports shop has a tennis racquet for £30, but the best one costs half as much again. How much is the best one?

19 You need £10 to buy a calculator, but you are 20% short. How much do you have?

20 What is 1.33 expressed as a fraction?

21 Your times for winning the 100 metres this term are 15 secs, 14 secs, 17 secs and 18 secs. What is your *average* time?

22 If you run twice round the perimeter of a rectangular field 70 m x 130 m, how far have

you run?

23 How many carpet squares 50 cm x 50 cm will be needed to cover a floor with an area of four square metres?

24 If you buy seventeen 10p balloons for a party, how much change will you have from £2?

25 If you scored $^{15}/_{15}$ on test 1A, two-thirds of that on test 4A and only half that on test 7A, what was your score on 7A?

√ X̶ ✗

		score
		25

How good are you at mental arithmetic?

How many stars?

	*	**	***
Age 9 or below	5 – 10	11 – 17	18 +
Age 10 – 11	7 – 12	13 – 19	20 +

ANSWERS

1A
1. 7
2. 6
3. 15
4. 4
5. 100
6. 7
7. 6
8. 12
9. 2
10. £1.20
11. 12
12. 0
13. 22
14. 3
15. £2

1B
1. 8
2. 6
3. 16
4. 3
5. 5
6. £2.35
7. 13
8. 9
9. 18
10. 10
11. 8
12. 50p
13. 25p
14. 17
15. 4

1C
1. 15
2. 5
3. 25
4. 5
5. 12
6. 90p
7. 18
8. 13
9. £1.60
10. 4
11. 10
12. £3
13. 30p
14. 1/2
15. 25p

1D
1. 15
2. 6
3. 16
4. 4
5. 12
6. 7
7. 13
8. 12
9. £1.60
10. £1.20
11. 8
12. £3
13. 25p
14. 3
15. 25p

2A
1. 13
2. 9
3. 24
4. 3
5. 10
6. £1.05
7. 11
8. 10
9. 50p
10. 3
11. 6
12. 75p
13. 20p
14. 1/4
15. 75p

2B
1. 18
2. 9
3. 28
4. 6
5. 6
6. 90p
7. 14
8. 19
9. 90p
10. 18
11. 8
12. 15
13. 40p
14. 2
15. $^{15}/_{20}$

2C
1. 12
2. 5
3. 16
4. 12
5. 22
6. 90p
7. 12 red
    10 blue
8. 23
9. £1
10. 50 mins
11. 12
12. £2.01
13. £1.50
14. 5
15. 30

2D
1. 12
2. 9
3. 28
4. 3
5. 22
6. £1.05
7. 14
8. 10
9. £1
10. 3
11. 8
12. £2.01
13. 40p
14. 1/4
15. 30